budgetbooks

CLASSIC ROCK

Exclusive Distributors:
Music Sales Limited
8/9 Frith Street, London W1D 3JB, England.
Music Sales Pty Limited
120 Rothschild Avenue, Rosebery, NSW 2018, Australia.

Order No. HLE90001945
ISBN 1-84449-110-2
This book © Copyright 2003 by Hal Leonard Europe

Printed in the USA

Your Guarantee of Quality
As publishers, we strive to produce every book to the highest commercial standards.
The book has been carefully designed to minimise awkward page turns and to make
playing from it a real pleasure.
Throughout, the printing and binding have been planned to ensure a sturdy, attractive
publication which should give years of enjoyment.
If your copy fails to meet our high standards, please inform us and we will gladly
replace it.

www.musicsales.com

Hal Leonard Europe
Distributed by Music Sales

CONTENTS

ALONE

Words and Music by BILLY STEINBERG
and TOM KELLY

Original key: Db major. This edition has been transposed up one half-step to be more playable.

How do I get ___ you a - lone? ___

D.S. al Coda

CODA

Oh, ___ oh, oh. _____ 'Til now ___ I

al - ways got by ___ on my own, ___ I nev - er real - ly cared un - til I met you.

And now it chills me to the bone. How do I get ___ you a - lone? ___

How do I get ___ you a - lone? ___

Guitar solo ad lib.

BABY, I LOVE YOUR WAY

Words and Music by
PETER FRAMPTON

But don't hes - i - tate, ___ 'cause your

love _____ won't ___ wait. ___

D.S. al Coda

ALONE AGAIN OR

Words and Music by
BRIAN MacLEAN

AUTHORITY SONG

Words and Music by
JOHN MELLENCAMP

Well, I ___ fight au - thor - i - ty. Au - thor - i - ty al - ways wins. ___

Well, I been do - in' it since ___ I was a

young kid, and I've come out grin - nin'. Well, I ___

___ fight au - thor - i - ty. Au - thor - i - ty al - ways wins. ___

BABA O'RILEY

Words and Music by
PETER TOWNSHEND

Out here ___ in the fields ___ I fight ___ for my meals, ___

I get my back ___ in-to ___ my liv - ing. ___ I don't need to fight ___

___ to prove I'm right; I don't need ___ to be for-giv-

Put out the fire___ and don't look past___ my shoul - der.___

The ex - o - dus is here;___ The hap-py ones are near.___

Let's get to-geth - er be - fore we get___ much old - er.___

CHORUS

Teen - age

BACK IN THE U.S.S.R.

Words and Music by JOHN LENNON
and PAUL McCARTNEY

Flew in from Mi - a - mi Beach, B.
Been a - way so long I hard - ly
Show me 'round your snow - peaked moun - tains

O. A. C., _ Did - n't get to bed last night. _ On _
knew the place, _ Gee _ it's good to get back home. _ Leave _
way down south, _ Take _ me to your dad - dy's farm. _ Let _

the way the pa- per bag was on my knee, Man
it till to- mor- row to un- pack my case, Hon-
me hear your bal- a- lai- kas ring- ing out, Come

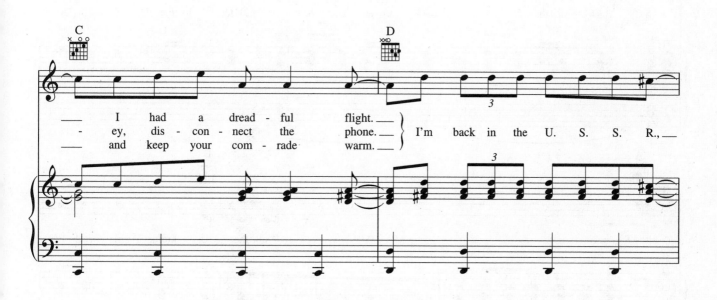

I had a dread- ful flight.
- ey, dis- con- nect the phone. I'm back in the U. S. S. R.,
and keep your com- rade warm.

You don't know how luck- y you are, boy.

BADGE

Words and Music by ERIC CLAPTON
and GEORGE HARRISON

love that you laid on my ta - ble.
kid. Now he's mar - ried to Ma - bel.
life since she fell out the cra - dle.

Yes, I told _____ you that the life goes up and down. _ Don't you no -

BALLROOM BLITZ

Words and Music by MIKE CHAPMAN
and NICKY CHINN

Oh, _____ yeah.   It was like

blitz,   ball - room   blitz,

BETH

Words and Music by PETER CRISS, BOB EZRIN
and STAN PENRIDGE

Rock Ballad, with feeling

Beth, I hear _ you call - in', but I can't come home right now. _
You say you feel _ so emp - ty, that our house just ain't a home. _

Me and the boys _ are play - in' and we just can't find the sound. _
I'm al - ways some - where else _ and _ you're al - ways there a - lone. _

Beth, I know __ you're lone - ly,   and I hope you'll be all right, __   'cause

me and the boys __ will be play - in'   all night.

BROWN EYED GIRL

Words and Music by
VAN MORRISON

Additional Lyrics

2. Whatever happened to Tuesday and so slow
Going down the old mine with a transistor radio
Standing in the sunlight laughing
Hiding behind a rainbow's wall
Slipping and a-sliding
All along the water fall
With you, my brown èyed girl
You, my brown eyed girl.
Do you remember when we used to sing:
Chorus

3. So hard to find my way, now that I'm all on my own
I saw you just the other day, my, how you have grown
Cast my memory back there, Lord
Sometime I'm overcome thinking 'bout
Making love in the green grass
Behind the stadium
With you, my brown eyed girl
With you, my brown eyed girl.
Do you remember when we used to sing:
Chorus

BLAZE OF GLORY

featured in the film YOUNG GUNS II

Words and Music by
JON BON JOVI

wake up   in the morn-ing and I   raise my wear-y head,____   I've got an
night I go to bed,   I pray the Lord my soul   to keep.__   No I ain't

Additional Lyrics (Album version)

2. When you're brought into this world
They say you're born in sin.
Well, at least they gave me something
I didn't have to steal or have to win.
Well, they tell me that I'm wanted
Yeah, I'm a wanted man.
I'm a colt in your stable,
I'm what Cain was to Abel.
Mister, catch me if you can.

BURNING LOVE

Words and Music by
DENNIS LINDE

Lord a-might - y,   I feel my tem - p'ra - ture ris - ing
Ooh hoo hoo,   I feel my tem - p'ra - ture ris - ing.

CALL ME THE BREEZE

Words and Music by
JOHN CALE

I ain't get me no - bod - y   I don't car - ry me no

load.   *Fine*

1. Ain't no   change   in the
2. 3. *(See additional lyrics)*

weath - er   Ain't no chang - es in   me.

There ain't no change   in the   weath - er,   ain't no

changes in me   And I ain't

hid - in' from no - bod - y,   no - bod - y's hid - in' from me.

1 This may be repeated **2,3**   **4**
ad lib. for instr.   (To Verses)   D. S. al Fine 𝄉

2. I got that   They

ADDITIONAL LYRICS

Verse 2.
    Well, I got that green light, baby
    I got to keep movin' on
    Well, I got that green light, baby
    I got to keep movin' on
    Well I might go out to California
    Might go down to Georgia, I don't know.

Verse 3.
    Well, I dig you Georgia peaches
    Makes me feel right at home
    Well, I dig you Georgia peaches
    Makes me feel right at home
    But I don't love me no one woman
    So I can't stay in Georgia long.

COME SAIL AWAY

Words and Music by
DENNIS DEYOUNG

Moderately slow, with feeling

set an o-pen course for the vir-gin sea. 'Cause I've got to_ be

free, free to face the life that's a-head of me.

COME TOGETHER

Words and Music by JOHN LENNON
and PAUL McCARTNEY

Here come old flat-top, He come groov-ing up slow-ly, He got Joo Joo eye-ball, He one ho-ly roll-er, He got hair down to his knee.

Got to be a jok-er, He just do what he please.

He wear no shoe-shine, He got
He Bag Pro-duc-tion, He got
He roll-er coast-er, He got

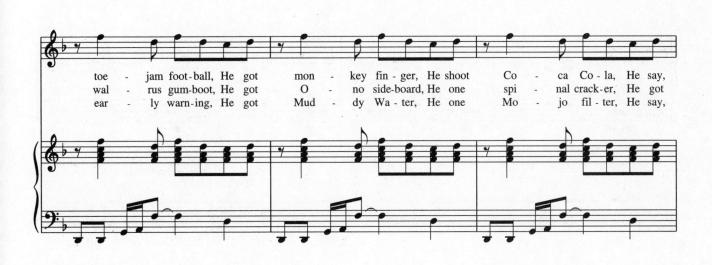

toe - jam foot-ball, He got mon - key fin - ger, He shoot Co - ca Co - la, He say,
wal - rus gum-boot, He got O - no side-board, He one spi - nal crack-er, He got
ear - ly warn-ing, He got Mud - dy Wa - ter, He one Mo - jo fil - ter, He say,

"I know _ you, you know me." _
feet down be - low_____ his knee. _
"One and one and one_____ is three." _

One thing I can tell you is you
Hold you in his arm-chair, you can
Got to be good look - ing 'cause he

DON'T DO ME LIKE THAT

Words and Music by
TOM PETTY

(1.) I was talk-in' with a friend of mine,   said a wom-an had   hurt his pride.___

(2.,D.S.)   Lis-ten hon-ey, can you see?   Ba-by, it would bur-y me___

DAY TRIPPER

Words and Music by JOHN LENNON
and PAUL McCARTNEY

Moderate Rock

E7

Got a good rea - son
She's a big tea - ser,
Tried to please_ her,

for

DON'T FEAR THE REAPER

Words and Music by
DONALD ROESER

88

DON'T LOOK BACK IN ANGER

Words and Music by
NOEL GALLAGHER

Verse 2:
Take me to the place where you go
Where nobody knows if it's night or day
Please don't put your life in the hands
Of a rock 'n' roll band who'll throw it all away.

I'm gonna start a revolution from my head
'Cause you said the brains I had went to my head
Step outside, the summertime's in bloom
Stand up beside the fireplace, take that look from off your face
'Cause you ain't never gonna burn my heart out.

DON'T STAND SO CLOSE TO ME

Written and Composed by
STING

DON'T STOP

Words and Music by
CHRISTINE McVIE

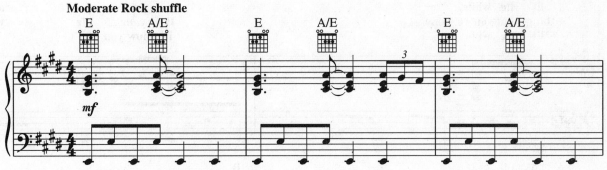

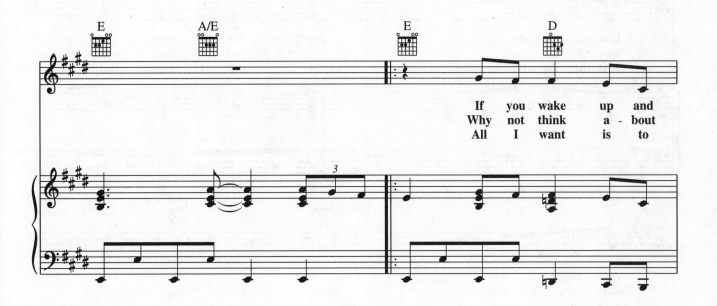

DREAM ON

Words and Music by
STEVEN TYLER

104

DREAMER

Words and Music by RICK DAVIES
and ROGER HODGSON

Lyrics:

Dream - er, you know you are a dream - er.

Well, can you put your hands in your head, oh no!

I said dream - er, you're noth-ing but a

114

you can do some - thing.) If I could do an - y - thing... (But can you do some - thing

out of this world?)

Take a dream on a Sun - day.

cresc. little by little

Can you put your hands in your head, oh no! Oh

no!

Fade out

Optional Ending

rit.

DRIVE MY CAR

Words and Music by JOHN LENNON
and PAUL McCARTNEY

Moderately, with a beat

Asked a girl what she
I told the girl that my
I told that girl I could

want - ed to be. ____ She said, "Ba - by, can't you see? ____
pros - pects were good, ___ And she said, "Ba - by, it's un - der - stood. ___
start right a - way, ___ And she said, "Lis - ten babe, I got some - thing to say.

I wan-na be fa - mous, a star of the screen, ___ But you can do some - thing
Work - ing for pea - nuts is all ver - y fine, ___ But I can show you a
I got no car and it's break ing my heart, ___ But I found a driv - er, and

EVERY BREATH YOU TAKE

Written and Composed by
G.M. SUMNER

long for your __ em-brace. I keep cry - ing, ba - by, ba - by, please__

EYE IN THE SKY

Words and Music by ALAN PARSONS
and ERIC WOOLFSON

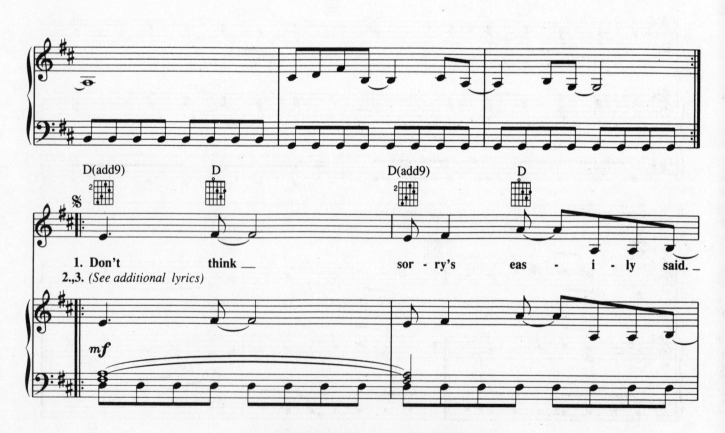

1. Don't   think __   sor - ry's   eas - i - ly   said. __

2.,3. (See additional lyrics)

part of me knows_ what you're think - ing.

I am the

eye in the sky, ___ look - ing at you; ___

___ I can read_ your mind. _ I am the mak - er of rules _

Additional Lyrics

2. Don't say words you're gonna regret.
Don't let the fire rush to your head.
I've heard the accusation before,
And I ain't gonna take any more,
Believe me.
The sun in your eyes
Made some of the lies worth believing.
(To Chorus:)

3. Don't leave false illusions behind.
Don't cry 'cause I ain't changing my mind.
So find another fool like before,
'Cause I ain't gonna live anymore believing
Some of the lies, while all of the signs are deceiving.
(To Chorus:)

GIVE A LITTLE BIT

Words and Music by RICK DAVIES
and ROGER HODGSON

FAITHFULLY

Words and Music by
JONATHAN CAIN

FOOLS GOLD

Words and Music by JOHN SQUIRE
and IAN BROWN

winds on through the hills— for fif - teen days.

The pack on my back is ach - ing, the

To Coda ⊕

straps seem to cut me like a knife.—

I'm watch-ing you all,___ I'm see-ing you sink - ing.

I'm stand-ing a - lone,___ you're weigh-ing your gold,___ I'm watch-ing you sink-

- ing.___ Fool's___ gold.

D.%. al Coda

3. These

⊕ *Coda*

Some-times you have to try___ to get a - long dear,

I know the truth and I___ know what you're think - ing.

Down, down,___ down,___ down, da down, down.

150

Repeat to fade

Verse 3:
These boots were made for walking
The Marquis de Sade never made no boots like these
Gold's just around the corner
Breakdown's coming up 'round the bend.

FREE BIRD

Words and Music by ALLEN COLLINS
and RONNIE VAN ZANT

To Coda

Lord knows I can't change.

(Instrumental)

D.C. al Coda

CODA

Lord, help me, I can't change.

GLORIA

Words and Music by
VAN MORRISON

Steady Rock

Like to tell you 'bout my ba - by.

here,

You know she __ comes 'round. __

just a - bout __ mid - night. __

Just 'bout five feet four __

Makes me feel so good Lord,

from her head to the

makes me feel __ al -

ground. __

right. ___

Well, she comes a - round here ___

Walk - in' down __ my street, ___

just a - bout mid -

comes up to my

GOODBYE YELLOW BRICK ROAD

Words and Music by ELTON JOHN
and BERNIE TAUPIN

GREEN-EYED LADY

Words and Music by JERRY CORBETTA,
J.C. PHILLIPS and DAVID RIORDAN

HEART AND SOUL

Words and Music by MIKE CHAPMAN
and NICKY CHINN

And if it got hot and hec - tic,___
Nine o'-clock this morn - ing,___

I know she'd be e - lec - tric___
She left with - out a warn - ing.___

I'd let her take her chanc -
I let her take ad - van -

- es___ with me.___ You see ___ she gets ___ what she ___ wants___
- tage ___ of me.___ You see ___ she got ___ what she want-ed ___

___} 'cause she's heart and soul, ___

she's hot and cold. ___

She's got it all, _____ hot lov-ing ev-'ry

night.

HEAT OF THE MOMENT

Words and Music by GEOFFREY DOWNES
and JOHN WETTON

HEAVEN

Words and Music by BRYAN ADAMS
and JIM VALLANCE

love is all ___ that I need, and I found it there ___ in your heart. It

is - n't too hard ___ to see ___ we're in heav - en, heav - en. _____

Optional Ending

ba - by, you're all ___ that I want when you're ly - in' here ___ in my arms. I'm

find - ing it hard ___ to be - lieve we're in heav - en.

I FEEL FINE

Words and Music by JOHN LENNON
and PAUL McCARTNEY

IF YOU LEAVE ME NOW

Words and Music by
PETER CETERA

I WANT TO KNOW WHAT LOVE IS

Words and Music by
MICK JONES

IN THE SUMMERTIME

Words and Music by
RAY DORSET

With a steady beat

Ch - ch-ch, uh! Ch - ch-ch, uh!

Ch - ch-ch, uh! Ch - ch-ch, uh! Ch - ch-ch, uh!

Ch - ch-ch, uh! Ch - ch-ch, uh! Ch - ch-ch, uh!

To Coda

drink, have a drive, go out and see ___ what you can
sun goes down ___ you can make it, make it good in a lay-
rich, if she's nice, bring your friends ___ and we'll all go in-to

find.

If her by.

We're no threat, peo - ple. We're not dirt - y, we're not mean. We love

ev - 'ry - bod - y, but we do as we please. ___ When the

Dah   dah __ dah,   dee dah do dee do do dah do dah.

Dah do dah dah   dah __   dah dah   dah __ do dah dah. __

D.S. al Coda

CODA

town.

LIKE A ROLLING STONE

Words and Music by
BOB DYLAN

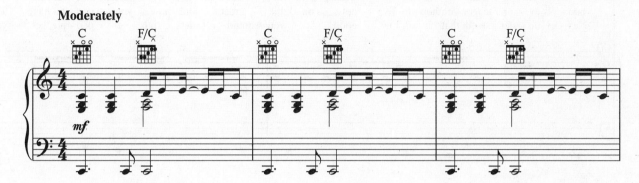

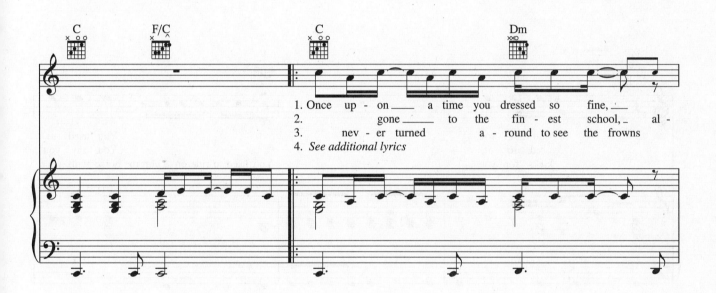

1. Once up-on ___ a time you dressed so fine, ___
2. ___ gone ___ to the fin-est school, ___ al-
3. ___ nev-er turned a-round to see the frowns
4. *See additional lyrics*

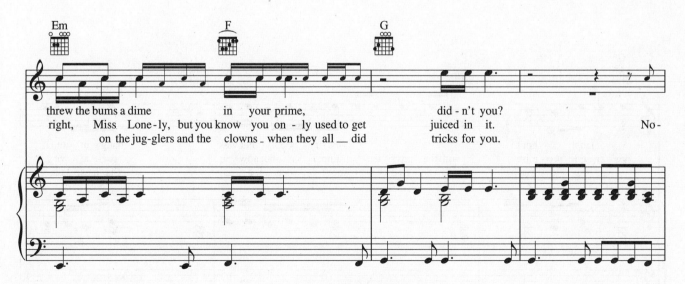

threw the bums a dime in your prime, did-n't you?
right, Miss Lone-ly, but you know you on-ly used to get juiced in it.
on the jug-glers and the clowns _ when they all _ did tricks for you. No-

Peo - ple call, say, __ "Be - ware, __ doll, you're bound to fall." You thought they were all
bod - y's ev - er taught you how to live out __ on the street __ and now __ you're gon - na have to get
Nev - er un - der - stood that it ain't no good __ you should - n't let __ oth - er peo - ple get your __

a - kid - din' you.
used to it.
kicks for you.

You used to
You say you
You used to ride on a chrome horse with your

laugh a - bout
nev - er com - pro - mise
dip - lo - mat

with the mys - ter - y tramp,
who car - ried on his shoul - der __ a __

ev - 'ry - bod - y that was
but now you
Sia - mese cat. __

hang - in' out. __
re - al - ize __

a com - plete un - known, _ like a roll - ing stone? _

Repeat and Fade | **Optional Ending**

Additional Lyrics

4. Princess on the steeple and all the pretty people
They're all drinkin', thinkin' that they got it made.
Exchanging all precious gifts,
But you better take your diamond ring,
You'd better pawn it, babe.
You used to be so amused
At Napoleon in rags and the language that he used.
Go to him now, he calls you, you can't refuse.
When you got nothin', you got nothin' to lose.
You're invisible now, you got no secrets to conceal.
Chorus

IT'S ONLY LOVE

Words and Music by BRYAN ADAMS
and JIM VALLANCE

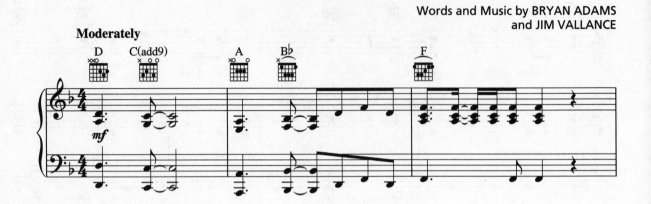

When the feel - in' is end - ed, there ain't
heart has been bro - ken, hard ____
shat - tered, ____ ain't ____

no use pre - tend - in'. Don't ya wor - ry,
words have been spo - ken, it ain't eas - y,
noth - in' else mat - ters. It ain't o - ver,

Well, it's on - ly love.
but it's on - ly love.
it's __ on - ly love.

When your
And if your
If your

THE JOKER

Words and Music by STEVE MILLER,
EDDIE CURTIS and AHMET ERTEGUN

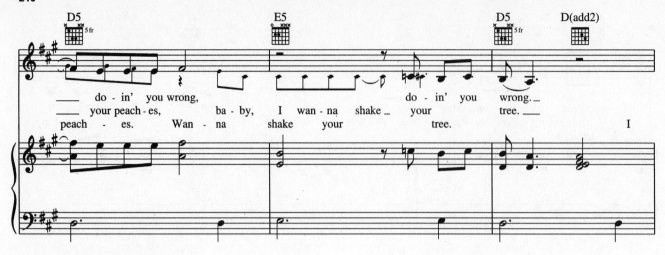

KNOCKIN' ON HEAVEN'S DOOR

Words and Music by
BOB DYLAN

THE LOVECATS

Words and Music by
ROBERT SMITH

1. We—

Verses 2:
We're so wonderfully, wonderfully, wonderfully
Wonderfully pretty
Oh you know that I'd do anything for you
We should have each other to tea huh?
                    2° (dinner)
We should have each other with cream
Then curl up in the fire and sleep for awhile
                    2° (get up for awhile)
It's the grooviest thing, it's a perfect dream.

Into the sea *etc.*

MATTHEW AND SON

By CAT STEVENS

2. Watch them run down to plat - form one and the eight thir - ty train _ to Mat-thew and Son.
(Verse 3 see block lyric)

Mat-thew and Son, the work's nev- er done, there's al-ways some-thing

new.

The files in your head, _ you take them

to bed, you're nev - er ev - er through. _____

And they've been

Verse 3:
And there's a five minute break
And that's all you take
For a cup of cold coffee
And a piece of cake.

Matthew and Son *etc.*

OLIVER'S ARMY

Words and Music by
ELVIS COSTELLO

PAPERBACK WRITER

Words and Music by JOHN LENNON
and PAUL McCARTNEY

Bright Rock

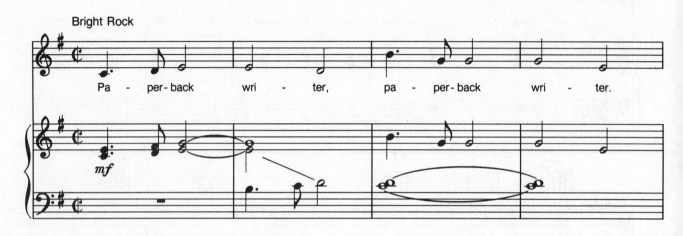

Pa - per - back wri - ter, pa - per - back wri - ter.

Dear__ Sir or Mad - am will you read my book? It took me
It's a thou - sand pag - es, give or take a few; I'll be

dirt - y man,___ and his cling - ing wife___ does - n't un - der-stand. His
have the rights,___ it could make a mil - lion for you o - ver-night. If you

son is work - ing for the Dai - ly Mail;___ It's a
must re - turn___ it you can send it here,___ But I

stead - y job___ but he wants to be a pa - per-back writ - er,___
need a break___ and I want to be a pa - per-back writ - er,___

C

G7

___ pa - per-back writ - er.
___ pa - per-back writ - er.___

PENNY LANE

Words and Music by JOHN LENNON
and PAUL McCARTNEY

239

RENEGADE

Words and Music by
TOMMY SHAW

Oh __ mam-ma I'm in fear for my life from the long ___ arm _ of the law. __
Law _ man has put an end to my run-ning and I'm so far __ from my home. __

hear you a-cry-ing, you're so scared and all a - lone. ___
down from the gal - lows and I don't have ver - y long.

Oh ___ mam - ma I'm in fear for my life from the long ___ arm ___ of the law. ___

Hang - man is com - ing down from the gal - lows and I don't have ___ ver - y long. ___

___ —

The jig is up, the news is out, ___ they

fi - nal - ly ___ found ___ me, the ren - e - gade ___ who had it made ___ re -

trieved for a boun - ty. Nev - er more to go ___ a - stray, ___

this will be the end_ to-day of the want-ed man,_____ want - ed man._

Guitar solo ad lib.

Repeat and Fade

Optional Ending

PICTURES OF LILY

Words and Music by
PETER TOWNSHEND

Li - ly, Oh Li - ly.   Pic-tures of Li - ly

Coda

For me and Li-ly are to - ge-ther in __ my dreams __

And I ask you, hey   Mis-ter have you ev-er   seen __   Pic-tures of Li - ly?

PINK HOUSES

Words and Music by
JOHN MELLENCAMP

There's a black man / with a black cat
young man / in a T - shirt
peo - ple / and more peo - ple.

liv - in' in a black neigh - bor - hood. __ He's got an
lis - t'nin' to a rock - in' roll - in' sta - tion. __ He's got
What do they know? __

in - ter - state___ run - nin' through___ his front yard.___ You know, he
greas - y hair___ and a greas - y smile___ that says, "Lord,
Go to work___ in some high - rise and va - ca - tion down at

F   C   G

thinks he's got it so good.___ And there's a
this must be my des - ti - na - tion." 'Cause they
the Gulf of Mex - i - co.___ And there's

wom - an in the kitch - en clean - in' up the eve - nin' slop.
told me when I was young - er, "Boy, you gon - na be Pres - i -
win - ners and there's los - ers, but they ain't no big deal.___

RADAR LOVE

Words and Music by GEORGE KOOYMANS
and BARRY HAY

I've been driv - in' all night. My hand's wet on the wheel.
ra - di - o was play-in' some for - got - ten song. —
No more speed, I'm al - most there.

There's a voice — in my head — that
Bren - da Lee — is
I got - ta keep cool now, I

drives my heel. ___
com-in' on strong. ___
got-ta take care. ___ It's my ba -
The road ___
Last ___

___ by call - in', said, "I need ___ you here." ___
___ has got ___ me hyp-no - tized. ___
___ car to pass, here ___ I go. ___

And it's half past four and I'm shift - in' gear. ___
And I'll be spit - ting in - to a new sun - rise. ___
And the line of cars drove down real slow. ___

260

The   ra - dar

love. _

Play 4 times

N.C.

D.S.S. al Coda II

And the

CODA II

Eb

in the sky.

Fm   Db   Ab

We've ____ got a thing ____ that's

Eb   Fm   Db

called ra-dar love. __   We've got a thing__

RHIANNON

Words and Music by
STEVIE NICKS

Rhi - an - non rings ___ like a bell through the night, and
She is ___ like a cat in the dark, and

would-n't you love to love ___ her? ___
then she is the dark - ness. ___
Takes to the sky like a
She rules her life like a

RIDERS ON THE STORM

Words and Music by
THE DOORS

To Coda

dog with-out a bone, an act-or out on loan. Rid-ers on the storm. ____

____ There's a kill-er on the road, _____ his brain is
got-ta love your man. _____ Girl, you

squirm-ing like a toad. _____ Take a long hol-i-day,
got-ta love your man. _____ Take him by the hand,

let your chil-dren play.
make him un-der-stand. If you
The

Repeat and Fade

ROCK 'N' ROLL STAR

Words and Music by
NOEL GALLAGHER

1, 2. I live my life in the ci-

ty, there's no ea-sy way out.

278

SHOW ME THE WAY

Words and Music by
PETER FRAMPTON

Moderately

I won-der how you're feel-ing. There's

I can see no rea-son. You're

ROXANNE

Written and Composed by
STING

RUNNING ON FAITH

Words and Music by
JERRY WILLIAMS

Late-ly, I've been run-nin' on _____ faith. _____
Late-ly, I've been talk - in' in _____ my sleep.

SHAKEDOWN
from the Paramount Motion Picture BEVERLY HILLS COP II

Words and Music by KEITH FORSEY,
HAROLD FALTERMEYER and BOB SEGER

(She's)
SOME KIND OF WONDERFUL

Words and Music by
JOHN ELLISON

Moderate Rock Shuffle

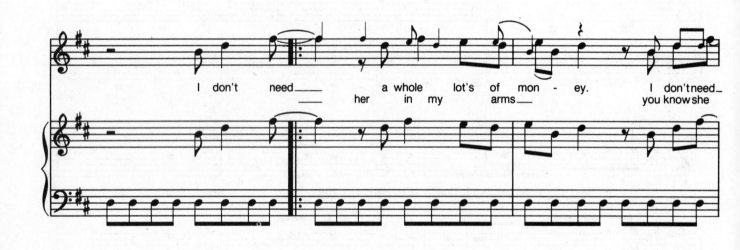

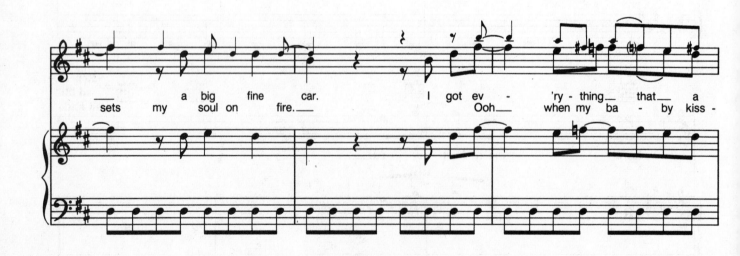

man   could want.   I got more___   than I could ask
es   me___   my heart be-comes   filled___ with de -

___ for.   I, I don't___ have   to
sire.___   When she wraps her lov-in' arms___ a-round___

run a-round.   I don't have___ to stay   out all   night.
___ me   it 'bout   have drives   me   out of my mind.___

305

SOMETHING IN THE AIR

Words and Music by
JOHN KEEN

Call out the in- sti- ga - tors be- cause there's some- thing in the air,—

we got to get— to- geth- er soon- er or lat - er be- cause— the

312

Hand out the arms and am - mo we're gon - na

blast our way through here,_____ we got to get___ to - geth - er soon - er or lat -

SUMMER OF '69

Words and Music by BRYAN ADAMS
and JIM VALLANCE

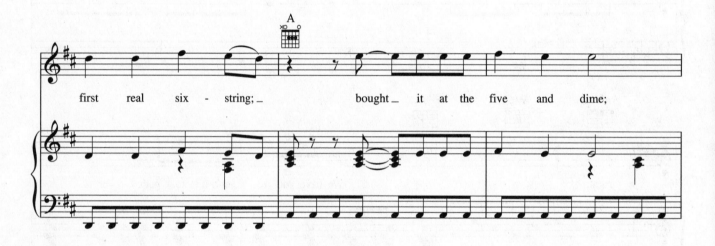

THROWING IT ALL AWAY

Words and Music by TONY BANKS,
PHIL COLLINS and MIKE RUTHERFORD

Need I say I love you
can-not live to-geth-er
Someday you'll be sor-ry

need I say I care
we cannot live a-part
someday when you're free

need I say that e-mo-tion's
that's the sit-u-a-tion I've
memories will re-mind you that

something we don't share
known it from the start
our love was meant to be

324

SWEET EMOTION

Words and Music by STEVEN TYLER
and TOM HAMILTON

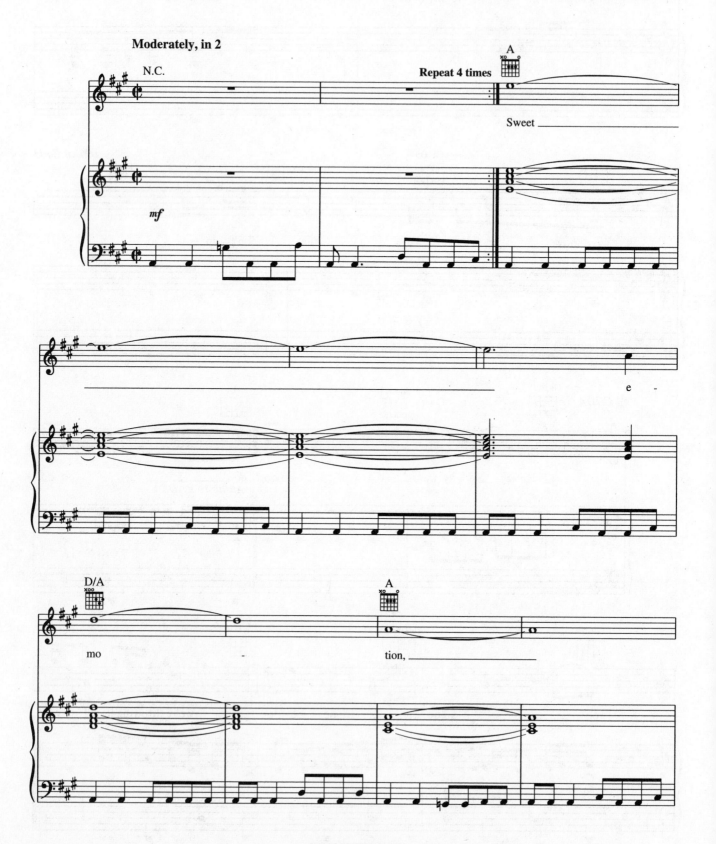

You're call - in' my name but I
Well, I got good news, she's a
You're tell - in' her things but your
I'm talk - in' 'bout some-thin' you can

got - ta make clear. _____
real good li - ar, _____
girl - friend lied; _____
sure un - der - stand, _____

I
'cause my
you
'cause a

can't say, ba - by, where I'll be in a year. _____
back - stage boo - gie set your pants on fire. _____
can't catch me 'cause the rab - bit done died. _____
month on the road and I'll be eat - in' from your hand. _____

TAKIN' CARE OF BUSINESS

Words and Music by
RANDY BACHMAN

ci - ty. There's a whis - tle up a - bove and peo - ple
mel - low. Get a sec - ond hand gui - tar____ chanc - es

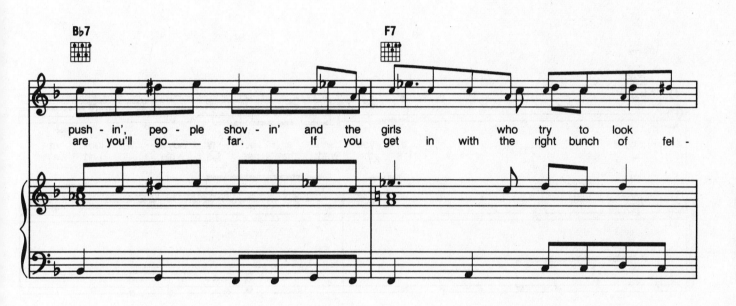

push - in', peo - ple shov - in' and the girls who try to look
are you'll go____ far. If you get in with the right bunch of fel -

pret - ty. And if your train's on time, you can
lows. Peo - ple see you hav - in' fun, just a

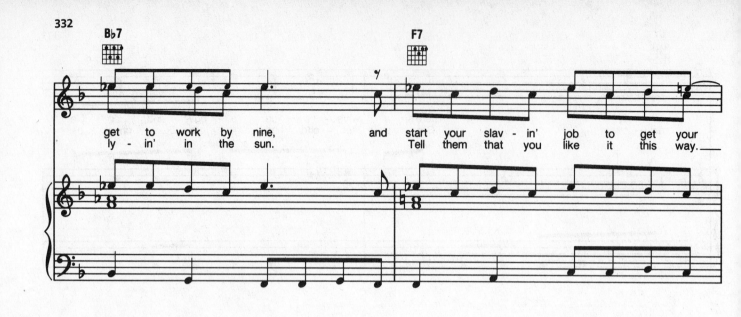

get to work by nine, and start your slav - in' job to get your
ly - in' in the sun. Tell them that you like it this your

pay.
— If you ev - er get an - noyed look at
It's the work that we a - void and we're

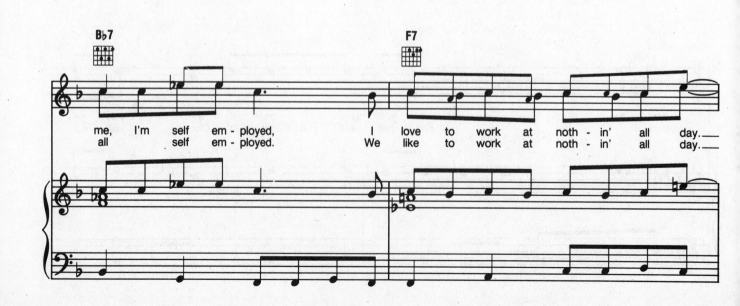

me, I'm self em - ployed, I love to work at noth - in' all day.
all self em - ployed. We like to work at noth - in' all day.

work - in' o - ver - time, work - out.
work - in' o - ver - time.

There's work

CODA   C7

no chord

work - in' o - ver - time.

Tak - in' care of busi - ness.

1-3   4   C(no3rd)   B♭(no3rd)

Tak–   Tak - in' care of busi - ness,

F(no3rd)   C(no3rd)

ev - 'ry day.___   Tak - in' care of busi - ness,

THESE EYES

Written by BURTON CUMMINGS
and RANDY BACHMAN

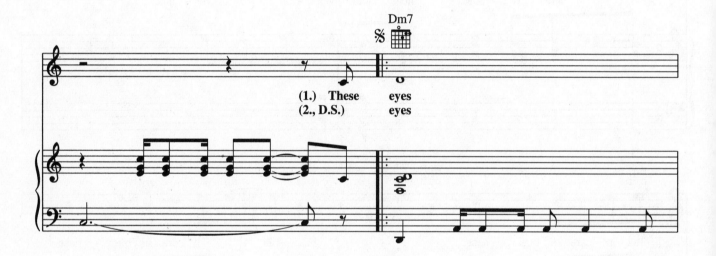

340

TIME FOR ME TO FLY

Words and Music by
KEVIN CRONIN

TWO OUT OF THREE AIN'T BAD

Words and Music by
JIM STEINMAN

Moderately slow, with a beat

Ba - by, we can talk all ___ night, ___

but that ain't get - ting us no - where.

I've told you ev - 'ry - thing I

pos - si - bly can; ___ there's noth - ing left in - side ___ of here. And

WALK OF LIFE

Words and Music by
MARK KNOPFLER

THE WEIGHT

By J.R. ROBERTSON

1. I pulled in-to Na-za-reth, was feel-in' 'bout half-past dead.
(Verses 2-5. see block lyrics)

I just need some place ___ where I can lay ___ my head. ___

Verse 2:
I picked up my bag, I went looking for a place to hide
When I saw Carmen and the Devil walking side by side
I said "Hey, Carmen, come on, let's go down town."
She said, "I gotta go but my friend can stick around."

Take a load off Fanny etc.

Verse 3:
Go down, Miss Moses, there's nothing you can say
It's just ol' Luke and Luke's waiting on the judgement day
"Well, Luke my friend, what about young Anna Lee?"
He said "Do me a favour son, won't you stay
    and keep Anna Lee Company?"

Take a load off Fanny etc.

Verse 4:
Crazy Chester followed me and he caught me in the fog
He said "I will fix your rack if you'll take Jack, my dog."
I said "Wait a minute Chester, you know a peaceful man."
He said "That's O.K. boy, won't you feed him when you can."

Take a load off Fanny etc.

Verse 5:
Catch a cannonball now, to take me down the line
My bag is sinking low and I do believe it's time
To get back to Miss Fanny, you know she's the only one
Who sent me here with her regards for everyone.

Take a load off Fanny etc.

YOU REALLY GOT ME

Words and Music by
RAY DAVIES

so I can't sleep at night. You real-ly got me.____ You real-ly got me.____ You real-ly got me.____

Oh, oh.____

YOU'RE THE DEVIL IN DISGUISE

Words and Music by BILL GIANT,
BERNIE BAUM and FLORENCE KAYE